HAMLET
LUCKY EDDIE
HÄGAR
HELGA
SNERT
HONI

YOU VIKINGS ARE JUST AS VIOLENT AND MEAN AS US HUNS! BUT WE GET THE BAD MOUTH!
BUT NOT THE VIKINGS— OH, NO! EVERYBODY LOVES THE VIKINGS! WHY? WHY?!
CLASS
DIK BROWNE

WHAT'S THIS ?!
IT'S CALLED "HELGA'S HEAVENLY HELPING OF HAPPINESS"

YOU JUST CAN'T SAY "LEFTOVER LIVER," CAN YOU ?!
DIK BROWNE

WHAT'S WRONG WITH IT? IT HAS PLENTY OF SUNLIGHT... I TALK TO IT...
DIK BROWNE
PROBABLY WATERING IT TOO MUCH

LIFE IS SHORT—AFTER I'M GONE I'D LIKE TO BE REMEMBERED BY DOING SOMETHING UNIQUE AND UNUSUAL...
WHY DON'T YOU BUY A ROUND OF DRINKS?
DIK BROWNE

HAGAR!
HUH ?!

IT'S ME— AVERY OF AVENDON!
AVERY! HOW ARE YOU?

I DIDN'T RECOGNIZE YOU!
WELL, I'VE LOST WEIGHT
DIK BROWNE

WHAT DID YOU DO WITH THE DIET I GAVE YOU LAST TIME?
TELL HIM! TELL HIM!!
MMMMM
DIK BROWNE

HE ATE IT!!
I WAS HUNGRY...

I'M HERE TO VISIT MY FRIEND
WHY IS HE HERE ?
HE SLIPPED ON A PEBBLE, FELL THROUGH A WINDOW, TUMBLED DOWN A FLIGHT OF STAIRS AND WAS HIT BY A WILD BULL ...
WHAT'S HIS NAME ?
LUCKY EDDIE
DIK BROWNE

I WISH YOU WOULDN'T GO TO ENGLAND SO MUCH...
DIK BROWNE

YOU ALWAYS COME HOME WITH A HEAD COLD!

NO, HELGA! I HAD A BATH!
NO!
SPLASH!

WELL, I FINALLY GOT HIM IN THE BATH-TUB... NOW THE TOUGH PART...
DIK BROWNE

GETTING HIS CLOTHES OFF

HAGAR! WHAT ARE YOU DOING IN THERE?
ER... JUST LOOKING FOR MY SWORD
DIK BROWNE

IT'S NOT IN THE COOKIE JAR!

HELGA! LOOK!!
DIK BROWNE

WHAT DO YOU WANT?

NOTHING...

I'VE DECIDED TO BUILD A BIGGER PLAYROOM
THAT'S VERY SUDDEN

WHAT MADE YOU DECIDE TO DO THAT ?

SIT!
DIK BROWNE
DO YOU HAVE TO DO EVERYTHING THE HARD WAY?

SOMETHING COOL AND REFRESHING
SCOTCH AND WATER

AHHHH!!
DIK BROWNE

LOOK! I'M LEARNING TO WRITE MY NAME!
NICE... BUT YOU DID IT UPSIDE DOWN
REALLY?
I'LL NEVER GET IT RIGHT

IS THE ENEMY IN SIGHT?
DEFINE "ENEMY"

NEVER PICK A PHILOSOPHER TO BE A LOOKOUT!
© DIK BROWNE

I DIDN'T KNOW HAGAR COULD READ
HE CAN'T— IT'S JUST A PICTURE BOOK

YOU GOT IT UPSIDE DOWN
DIK BROWNE

LET ME HAVE ONE FOR THE ROAD
OKAY

DIK BROWNE

NOW LET'S HAVE ONE FOR THE SKY
I THINK YOU'VE HAD ENOUGH

HI YA, HONEY! I'M HOME AT LAST FROM THE LONG SEA VOYAGE!

BOY, THE KID'S SURE HAVE GROWN!
THOSE ARE THE NEIGHBORS!
DIK BROWNE

DON'T WIGGLE! I'M ALMOST FINISHED
CLIP!
CLIP!
DIK BROWNE

THERE! IT'S DONE!

WAS I GOOD?
PRETTY GOOD

DIK BROWNE

HEEL!

I'M BACK FROM HUNTING!
OH, GOOD! WHAT'S IN THE BAG?

DIK BROWNE
EVER COOK FROG LEGS?

'DIN-DIN', SNERT!

LUCKY DOG! YOU GOT IT MADE! YOU DON'T HAVE TO USE YOUR BRAIN— SOMEONE WILL FEED YOU!

'DIN-DIN', HAGAR!
DIK BROWNE

IT'S ABOUT TIME YOU GOT HOME FROM WORK — DINNER IS ON THE TABLE!
DIK BROWNE

IS IT OKAY IF I HAVE A DRINK AND UNWIND FIRST ?

WHY *CAN'T* WIVES GO ON BUSINESS TRIPS?
*BECAUSE*- THEY'D BE BORED

AND YOU WERE AFRAID *I'D* BE BORED?
YES

HOW SWEET
DIK BROWNE

MAMA, IS IT TRUE THAT WOMEN INVENTED CIVILIZATION ?
OF COURSE
DIK BROWNE

DO YOU THINK ANY MAN WOULD TAKE HIS ELBOWS OFF THE TABLE UNLESS SOME WOMAN TOLD HIM TO ?

WHAT HAS 8 LEGS, 3 HEADS AND LIKES TO EAT PICKLES ?
I DON'T KNOW— WHAT DOES ?
I DON'T KNOW EITHER
WHAT HAS 8 LEGS 3 HEADS AND LIKES TO EAT PICKLES ?
DIK BROWNE

MY SIDE IS ALMOST FINISHED!
MINE TOO!

DIK BROWNE
UH-OH!

DAD, DO I HAVE TO BE A VIKING?
OF COURSE — OUR FAMILY HAS BEEN IN LOOTING AND PLUNDER-ING FOR GENERATIONS

ISN'T THERE ANYTHING ELSE I COULD DO?
I'M NOT SURE...

HOW ABOUT POLITICS?

WHATEVER HAPPENED TO YOUR PROMISE TO CLIMB THE HIGHEST MOUNTAIN AND SWIM THE DEEPEST RIVER FOR ME ?

I THREW OUT MY BACK CARRYING YOU OVER THE THRESHOLD, REMEMBER ?
DIK BROWNE

IN JUDGING WINE, THREE THINGS ARE IMPORTANT
1-COLOR 2-AROMA -AND FINALLY 3-TASTE...
SLURP!
3 IS THE BIGGIE
DIK BROWNE

DON'T PICK AT YOUR FOOD, HAMLET!
MOTHER IS RIGHT, SON
STAB AT IT LIKE THIS!
DIK BROWNE

WHY CAN'T WE GET MARRIED, LUTE?
I DON'T HAVE A JOB, HONI— WHERE WOULD WE LIVE?
RIGHT HERE WITH MOMMY AND DADDY!
OKAY! OKAY! WE'LL WAIT TILL YOU GET A JOB!
DIK BROWNE

THERE ARE ONLY TWO KINDS OF PEOPLE IN THIS WORLD, LUCKY EDDIE, — GOOD PEOPLE AND BAD PEOPLE
DIK BROWNE

IN CASE YOU'RE WONDERING — WE'RE GOOD PEOPLE

I WISH YOU'D WARN ME WHEN YOU BRING A GANG HOME FOR DINNER!

DIK BROWNE
YOU TOO !!

CLIP CLIP
CLIP

CLIP CLIP
CLIP CLIP

CLIP
CLIP
CLIP
CLIP
CLIP
CLIP
CLIP

PUFF I GIVE UP... IT'S GROWING FASTER THAN I CAN CUT IT!!

DON'T BREAK THAT MIRROR, LUCKY EDDIE... YOU DON'T WANT ANY BAD LUCK
DON'T WORRY
MY LUCK COULDN'T GET WORSE...
DIK BROWNE

ENJOY! TODAY IS LEIF ERICSON'S DAY!
VIKINGS DON'T WORK ON LEIF ERICSON'S BIRTHDAY!

I'LL BET MRS. ERICSON DOES!

I AM HÄGAR THE HORRIBLE! I'M AS TOUGH AS A CROCODILE, MEAN AS A WILDCAT, AND ROUGHER THAN BOTH IN A BAG!
DIK BROWNE

WHAT'S WRONG?

YOU'RE SUPPOSED TO INTRODUCE ME FIRST.

THIS IS THE POINT IN MY SPEECH WHERE I ALWAYS MENTION THAT EACH APPLICANT HAS AN EQUAL CHANCE TO BE PICKED AS A VIKING WARRIOR
DIK BROWNE

HOWEVER...

NICE CHURCH, BROTHER OLAF
PARDON ME, HAGAR, THAT MUST BE THE NEW CLEANING LADY...
DING
DONG

I DON'T DO WINDOWS

HMMM... A STRANGER CARRYING A BIG BOOK

I HAVE COME TO COMBAT IGNORANCE, SUPERSTITION, SIN AND INTEMPERANCE!

HAGAR! SOMEONE TO SEE YOU!
DIK BROWNE

GET OUTTA MY WAY!
MEAN MAX! YOU SHOULDN'T YELL AT THOSE FLOWERS FOR NO REASON!

THEY BUG ME!
AS LONG AS YOU HAVE A GOOD REASON!
DIK BROWNE

SCRAM! YOU LITTLE CREEP! I KNOW WHAT YOU WANT!

YA CAN'T WAIT TO TELL HELGA I HAD A DRINK! SNITCHER!
NOW GET LOST!

I MUST BE GOING NUTS! I'M TALKING TO A DUCK!!
WHAT DO YOU THINK OF THAT?!

WHAT'S THIS ?
I GOT A GOOD BUY IN CHICKEN PARTS AT THE MARKET

BUT THESE ARE CHICKEN CLAWS!
THAT'S WHY IT WAS SUCH A GOOD BUY
DIK BROWNE

SIGH THIS IS THE LIFE

BROWNE

DARNED FISH!

THIS IS DUMB! WATER DIETS NEVER WORK!

THIS ONE WILL!
DIK BROWNE

WHAT KIND OF BAIT ARE YOU USING ?
PEARLS

I'M FISHING FOR MERMAIDS
DIK BROWNE

TAKE OFF THOSE CLOTHES! IT'S TIME FOR A BATH!

DIK BROWNE

HOLD IT!
YOU'D BETTER TAKE YOUR CLOTHES IN WITH YOU!

KNUTE IS IN THE WRONG BUSINESS
WHAT DOES HE DO?

DIK BROWNE
HE LIVES BY HIS WITS
PLOP!

WHAT DO YOU DO WITH ALL THE MONEY I GIVE YOU ?
DIK BROWNE
WHERE DOES IT GO?! ANSWER ME!
AND STOP POKING ME IN THE STOMACH!

HAGAR GETS AS MUCH FUN OUT OF CHRISTMAS AS A KID!
I KNOW... WHAT'S HE DOING NOW?

HE'S SHOWING HAMLET HOW TO USE HIS NEW SLED
DIK BROWNE

DOES EVERYBODY HAVE A STAR, DAD?
SURE! THAT ONE IS MINE
SEE HOW BIG AND ROUND AND BRIGHT IT IS?
THAT'S THE MOON
SO WHAT?! IT'S STILL MINE!

SHOULD YOU BE "GIRL WATCHING" ?
AW, IT DOESN'T HURT TO LOOK

ARE YOU SURE ?
DIK BROWNE

WHY DON'T YOU LIKE WATER?
I LOVE WATER– IN ITS PLACE!

IF IT WEREN'T FOR WATER, WE VIKINGS WOULD HAVE TO WALK TO WORK!
DIK BROWNE

COME HERE! I HAVE SOMETHING TO SAY!
DIK BROWNE

BUT I DON'T WANT ANYONE TO HEAR IT— UNDERSTAND?
YEP!

I DON'T MEAN YOU, STUPID!
EH?

WHAT A FOUL PLACE!
LET'S GO TO A RIVER AND WASH!

M'LORD – THIS IS THE RIVER

NICE DOGS YOU GOT, SVEN. WHAT BREED ARE THEY ?

WATCHDOGS

YOU KNOW WHAT I MISS ?
WHAT ?

THE JOYS OF MARRIED LIFE
AREN'T YOU MARRIED ?

YEAH, BUT SO FAR I'VE MISSED THE JOYS
DIK BROWNE

WHAT ARE YOU — A BARBARIAN? USE YOUR FORK!
DIK BROWNE
THE LITTLE ONE!

WHAT'S FOR DINNER ?
HOW DOES ROAST BEEF SOUND ?
GREAT!
WE'LL HAVE THE ROAST BEEF.
DIK BROWNE

IS THERE A MAN WHOSE HEART WOULD SWELL TO CHARGE INTO THE MOUTH OF HELL ?

WHO SNEERS AT DANGER AND DEADLY FATE

GO TELL MY WIFE THAT I'LL BE LATE

I SAY, OLD CHAP— WOULD YOU MIND TERRIBLY IF WE WERE TO TRY TO SACK YOUR CASTLE ?
NOT AT ALL, OLD CHAP! GIVE IT A GO!
DIK BROWNE

IN ENGLAND MANNERS ARE VERY IMPORTANT!

YOU SHOULD GET MARRIED, HONI. BEING A VIKING ISN'T FOR WOMEN!

THEY LACK THE STRENGTH AND POWER TO BE WARRIORS—

USUALLY...
DIK BROWNE

WHERE WERE YOU ?
THE FLEA MARKET
DIK BROWNE

DID YOU GET ANYTHING ?
I THINK SO...

HOW'S THIS?!
NO! NO!

LUCKY EDDIE, I'LL TELL IT TO YOU JUST ONE MORE TIME!

"SPEAK SOFTLY AND CARRY A BIG STICK"
DIK BROWNE

EITHER YOU NEED A NEW HAT OR A SPRING TONIC
DIK BROWNE

SOMETIMES I WONDER WHAT DOGS THINK ABOUT...

THEY'RE SO MUCH LIKE HUMANS. DO THEY WORRY? DAYDREAM? PLAN?

DIK BROWNE
SOMETIMES I WONDER...

THE OLAFS GOT A DIVORCE
NO! WHAT HAPPENED ?

HE CAME HOME FROM OUR VOYAGE AND HIS WIFE SERVED HIM FISH!
LET'S GO OUT FOR DINNER
DIK BROWNE

I FINALLY FINISHED MY CHRISTMAS SHOPPING LIST!
DIK BROWNE

NOW I'VE GOT TO MAKE ONE FOR THE REST OF YOU

I'VE GOT A BITE!
ME TOO!!
SPLASH!
CHOMP!
SPLASH!
CHOMP!
CHOMP!
SPLASH!
HUNGRY LITTLE DEVILS, AREN'T THEY?
DIK BROWNE

THERE ARE SEVEN DEADLY SINS– PRIDE, COVETOUSNESS, LUST, ANGER, GLUTTONY, ENVY AND SLOTH
ARE YOU SURE?
I COULD HAVE SWORN ONE WAS "NAGGING"
DIK BROWNE

OH, LOOK! HAGAR'S FALLEN ASLEEP! I'M AFRAID HE'LL SPILL HIS BEER!
I'LL GET IT!
ZZZ

DIK BROWNE
GRRRRRRRR!
ZZZZ

DO YOU REALIZE YOU MISSED DINNER ?!
NO KIDDING!

I WASN'T EVEN AIMING AT IT

THIS IS GOING TO BE AN INTERESTING EVENING
DIK BROWNE

WHEN YOU COME RIGHT DOWN TO IT, THE MOST IMPORTANT THING IN LIFE IS LOVE
YOU'RE RIGHT
DIK BROWNE

I KNOW, I'D LOVE ANOTHER BEER

HOW MANY MILES TO THE GALLON DO YOU GET ?
22

24 IF WE USE VODKA
DIK BROWNE

WHY'D WE COME ALL THIS WAY UP HERE ?
I DIDN'T WANT TO WAKE MY FOLKS

HONI- WILL YOU MARRY ME ?

YES!
DIK BROWNE

YOU'RE IN A BUSINESS WHERE YOU MAKE A LOT OF ENEMIES!
DIK BROWNE

HOW DID SHE KNOW THAT?
IT'S A GIFT!

PAY THIS BILL OR *ELSE!*

"OR ELSE" WHAT?
DIK BROWNE

AW, THE ENGLISH AIN'T SO TOUGH

THEY PUT THEIR PANTS ON ONE LEG AT A TIME, SAME AS EVERYBODY

PRESENT COMPANY EXCEPTED, OF COURSE
DIK BROWNE

TAKE OFF MY ARMOR
YES, SQUIRE
DIK BROWNE

MEATBALLS? ARE YOU NUTS?!
BUT YOU LIKE MEATBALLS!

NOT DURING A STORM!

A BALLOON FOR MY KID
50 SILVER COINS

50 SILVER COINS?! THAT'S CRAZY! WHAT MAKES A DUMB BALLOON COST SO MUCH?
DIK BROWNE

INFLATION

LEARNING TO COOK TAKES TIME, HONI — WHY, I'LL NEVER FORGET THE FIRST MEAL I EVER SERVED...
I WON'T EITHER

DIK BROWNE
SHE BURNED THE SALAD

NO SIGN OF GAME...
I'M GOING TO TRY A BLAST

I'LL TRY ONE, TOO
DIK BROWNE

WHAT'S THIS STUFF?
HOMEMADE PEAS AND CARROTS BRANDY
YOU'LL DO ANYTHING TO MAKE ME EAT MY VEGETABLES, WON'T YOU?
DIK BROWNE

I WISH PEOPLE WOULD LEAVE MY THINGS ALONE!
I DON'T TOUCH OTHER PEOPLE'S PROPERTY AND I WISH THEY WOULDN'T TOUCH MINE!
THAT'S A FUNNY THING FOR A VIKING TO SAY
DIK BROWNE

IT'S TERRIBLE! HAGAR EATS LIKE A HORSE!
YOU MEAN HE'S THAT HUNGRY?
DIK BROWNE

I MEAN HE EATS LIKE A HORSE!

WHY CHASE FAME AND GLORY ?!

ALL THINGS COME TO HE WHO WAITS!

THIS LOOKS LIKE A GOOD PLACE TO WAIT
BAR
DIK BROWNE

WHAT A BEAUTIFUL VIEW!
YOU CAN SAY THAT AGAIN!

WHAT A BEAUTIFUL VIEW!
ECHO VALLEY
DIK BROWNE

YOU HAD SPAGHETTI... TWO BEERS... WAS KISSED ON THE CHEEK BY SOMEONE WEARING CHEAP ROUGE... AND HAD AN ICE-CREAM CONE — AND DON'T DENY IT!

DIK BROWNE
A MAN WITH A BEARD HAS NO SECRETS

YOU KING ARTHUR?
YEAH

IS THIS YOUR ROUND TABLE?
YEAH

WOW! SEE HOW PEOPLE EXAGGERATE?
DIK BROWNE

LOOK, SNERT! I'M GOING TO WALK IN BACKWARDS!
THEN IF HELGA CATCHES ME SHE'LL THINK I WAS ON MY WAY OUT!

CLEVER?
DIK BROWNE

GOT EVERYTHING?
YEP...

PIG TAILS, OWL'S FEET, SQUID BEAKS AND THE NOSE HAIRS OF A BLUE-WINGED BAT...

I KNOW IT COSTS A LITTLE MORE, BUT I BELIEVE IN USING NATURAL INGREDIENTS
DIK BROWNE

WHAT'S THAT?
WE RAN OUT OF BOILING OIL, SO WE'RE USING THE WATER HELGA USED TO WASH YOUR CLOTHES
BY GOLLY... THEY'RE SURRENDERING!
DIK BROWNE

WHEN THE DAY IS BAD AND LIFE'S A CURSE—
DIK BROWNE
CHEER UP!
TOMORROW MAY BE WORSE

GO SEE WHAT IT'S LIKE OUTSIDE
RIGHT

THERE'S A LOT OF GRASS AND SKY AND ROCKS OUT THERE
DIK BROWNE

DIK BROWNE

GUESS WHO ?!

WERE YOU EXPECTING ANYONE, DEAR ?
NO...
POUND!
POUND!

IT MUST BE FOR YOU...
DIK BROWNE

YOU DON'T LIKE HERRINGS ?
I GUESS I JUST DON'T LIKE FISH -

PRESENT COMPANY EXCEPTED, OF COURSE.
DIK BROWNE

BUY NICEY NICE RUG ?
I'LL BUY 'EM ALL!

I'LL SELL ALL BUT ONE

I NEED THIS ONE TO GET HOME
DIK BROWNE

THAT FELLOW LUTE IS A PUBLIC SCANDAL!
PICKING ON A YOUNG GIRL LIKE HONI!

HONI! LET ME GO—PLEASE! YOU'RE HURTING MY BACK!
DIK BROWNE

SIGH WOMEN BARTENDERS
I'LL HAVE ANOTHER ONE
NOT TILL YOU EAT YOUR VEGETABLES!
DIK BROWNE

THE GUESTS WILL BE HERE ANY MINUTE! GET CLEANED UP!!
GRUMBLE
DIK BROWNE

HAGAR!
NOW WHAT?!

DIK BROWNE
WELL, WHAT DO YOU WANT, SNERT ?

YOU WANT TO GO OUT ?

REMEMBER, MY BOY... "TREAT OTHERS AS YOU WOULD EXPECT THEM TO TREAT YOU—"

DIK BROWNE

BUT DO IT FIRST!

MY HEAD IS BUZZING, DOCTOR
I'D BETTER TAKE A LOOK

AHA!!
BZZZZ...
DIK BROWNE

ER...COULD ...I...ER... BUY YOU A DRINK, MISS?
WELL... ORDINARILY I DON'T LET JUST ANYBODY BUY ME A DRINK

BUT YOU LOOK LIKE MY THIRD HUSBAND. SO...OKAY
REALLY? HOW MANY TIMES HAVE YOU BEEN MARRIED?

TWICE
HAGAR!
DIK BROWNE

HAGAR! DON'T WALK ON MY CLEAN FLOOR WITH YOUR DIRTY FEET!
UH... HOLD IT!
DIK BROWNE

HERE'S YOUR DOGGIE BAG, SIR
THANK YOU

DIK BROWNE-
WOOF!

BEING A VIKING AIN'T WHAT IT USED TO BE! IT COSTS MORE TO RAID THAN YOU GET BACK!
AND ALL YOU GET IS TROUBLE— BUT THIS IS THE FINAL STRAW!
A PARKING TICKET!
DIK BROWNE

OF COURSE I'LL BE SAFE WHILE YOU'RE AWAY. SNERT WILL ...

PROTECT ME

WE'RE GONNA LOSE!
YOU'RE SUCH A DEFEATIST!

YOU DON'T HAVE ANY VISION! IMAGINATION! YOU GOTTA TAKE THE LONG VIEW!
DIK BROWNE

WE'RE GONNA DIE!?

HAGAR! THAT SOUP IS SEASONED ENOUGH!

TOO MUCH SALT IS BAD FOR YOU!
DIK BROWNE

LIKE MY NEW SUIT?
LOVE IT! WHERE DID YOU GET IT?

HODO THE MAGICIAN
DIK BROWNE

YOU'VE GOT EAR FATIGUE!
DIK BROWNE

YOU NEED A PERIOD OF SILENCE. AVOID ALL WITTY TALK, JOKES, TITTLE-TATTLE AND POETRY...

...AND STAY OUT OF IRELAND FOR A WHILE...

DIK BROWNE
OH...DEAR...

WHY CAN'T YOU BURY BONES LIKE OTHER DOGS ?

HI, HAGAR! WHA'CHA DOING WITH SNERT ?
TEACHING HIM TO HEEL

YOU WORK AND WORK AND WORK, AND WHAT DO YOU GET?
TIRED?
DIK BROWNE

VINCENT, WHY ARE ALL YOUR DRESSES BLACK THIS YEAR?
THAT'S ALL THEY'RE SHOWING IN PARIS, MADAM

DIK BROWNE
IT'S CALLED "THE DARK AGES LOOK"

WITH JUST TWO CREWS, I'M BOOKED TO INVADE TEN COUNTRIES IN SIX MONTHS! THAT'S A LOT!!

I HOPE I'M NOT SPREADING MYSELF TOO THIN

NOT TO WORRY
DIK BROWNE

IT'S BAD ENOUGH YOU'VE GOT US LIVING IN A HUT WITH A DIRT FLOOR...
YOU COULD AT LEAST CUT THE GRASS!
DIK BROWNE

I WISH YOU GAVE AS MUCH ATTENTION TO ME AS YOU DO THAT DUMB BOAT!

WHY? YOU GOT BARNACLES?
DIK BROWNE

## A selection of HÄGAR® books published by Ravette

**POCKET BOOKS**

| | |
|---|---|
| TRIES AGAIN | £2.50 |
| HAS A GO | £2.50 |
| IN A FIX | £2.50 |
| ALL AT SEA | £2.50 |
| ON THE RAMPAGE | £2.50 |
| GETS IT ALL | £2.50 |
| IN THE ROUGH | £2.50 |
| TAKES A BREAK | £2.50 |
| ON HOLIDAY | £2.50 |
| TAKES AIM | £2.50 |
| IN A STEW | £2.50 |
| MEASURE FOR MEASURE | £2.50 |
| SAYS IT WITH FLOWERS | £2.50 |
| CHIPS AWAY | £2.50 |
| LOOKS AHEAD | £2.50 |

**ALBUMS**

| | |
|---|---|
| THE HERO | £2.50 |
| LETS HIMSELF GO | £2.50 |

**BLACK AND WHITE LANDSCAPES**

| | |
|---|---|
| MEETS HIS MATCH | £2.50 |
| IN A HURRY | £2.50 |

**COLOUR LANDSCAPES**

| | |
|---|---|
| TELLS IT LIKE IT IS | £2.95 |
| NEVER SAY DIE | £2.95 |
| MAKES AN ENTRANCE | £2.95 |
| WELCOME HOME | £2.95 |

**COLOUR THEME BOOKS**

| | |
|---|---|
| No. 1 THE GREAT GOURMET | £2.95 |
| No. 2 TROUBLE AND STRIFE | £2.95 |
| No. 3 TAKES A JOURNEY | £2.95 |
| No. 4 CHILD'S PLAY | £3.50 |
| No. 5 WHO DARES WINS | £3.50 |

| | |
|---|---|
| VIKING HANDBOOK | £3.95 |

All these books are available at your local bookshop or newsagent, or can be ordered direct from the publisher. Just tick the titles you require and fill in the form below. Prices and availability subject to change without notice.

---

Ravette Books Limited, 3 Glenside Estate, Star Road, Partridge Green, Horsham, West Sussex RH13 8RA

Please send a cheque or postal order and allow the following for postage and packing. UK: Pocket books – 45p for one book plus 20p for the second book and 15p for each additional book. Landscape series – 50p for one book plus 30p for each additional book. Other titles – 85p for one book plus 60p for each additional book.

Name ..............................................................................................

Address ..........................................................................................

......................................................................................................